HOLIDAY HOOP
Flannel Board Fun

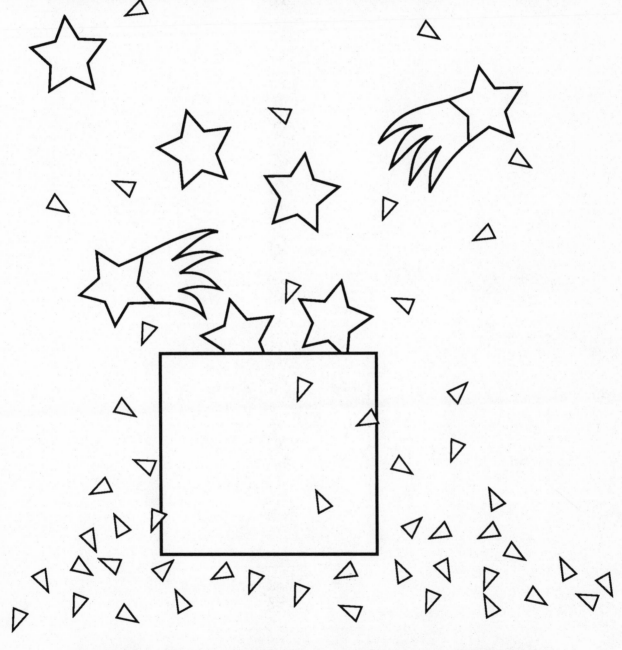

RHYMING FLANNEL BOARD STORIES
WITH LEARNING ACTIVITIES

by Kathy Darling, illustrated by Marilynn G. Barr

With special thanks to Cindy Ricca
and Ricca Family Day Care

Publisher: Roberta Suid
Editor: Carol Whiteley
Production: Susan Pinkerton

monday
morning®

Monday Morning is a registered trademark of
Monday Morning Books, Inc.

ISBN 1-878279-14-9

For information about our audio products, write us at:
Newbridge Book Clubs, 3000 Cindel Drive, Delran, NJ   08370

Printed in the United States of America
9 8 7 6 5 4 3 2 1

Contents

Introduction

Telling tales on a flannel board can help bring any holiday to life! *In Holiday Hoopla: Flannel Board Fun,* you will find everything from cheerful Christmas mice to a sly tale of April Fool's trickery between Toad and Donkey. You will find adaptations of American Indian, Japanese, German, Afro-American, and other tales, as well as some new and original stories. Though flannel board stories can be told and retold, they always seem fresh because young children can become a part of the story, moving patterns about the board and helping with sound effects. It is not unusual, after hearing a flannel board story, for children to pick up the pieces and retell the story again, in their own words, adding imaginative details of their own.

First create a flannel board by securing a large flannel piece, at least 2' by 3', to plywood, cardboard, cork, or heavy poster board. Use vinyl duct tape or a staple gun to hold the flannel in place. Throwing the flannel piece over the back of a chair or large bolster pillow is also convenient, and does away with storage problems. Keep several large pieces of colored flannel available for different backgrounds.

The patterns for our stories are meant to be copied or traced and then transferred to pieces of felt or sturdy paper. Once the shapes are cut, follow the patterns to add detail. I strongly suggest making all felt pieces. These days felt comes in vibrant colors, adds a lifelike dimension different from any picture book, and has a nice "feel." Felt pieces can also overlap on the board and still stay in place. They can be ironed if they become wrinkled or bent.

To make the pieces:

1. Cut each pattern out in felt and use a combination of marking pens and felt pieces to add detail. For example, in "The First Easter Bunny," cut out white felt eggs, then glue on blue felt stripes and orange felt dots. Use a good craft glue and set the pieces on a cookie sheet in a very low oven to set the glue.

2. If you simply must get your artistic fingers into some markers, transfer each pattern onto sturdy white paper and color away. The paper can be laminated to protect it. Glue a large square of sandpaper or felt to the back of each piece so that it will adhere to the board.

Read through all the stories first, taking special note of any reference to color so that you can add the right details when creating your pieces. "The Big-Hearted Elephant" calls for pink and gray ears glued back to back. You may have to improvise with two sets of ears if you use paper patterns. Also think about what sound effects you might like to add and what props to have on hand. For instance, in "The Magic Mortar" you might toss real rice kernels into the air. Or you might like to let the children snack on rice cakes during the story. "The Morning Before Christmas" calls for jingle bells, confetti, and glitter.

Practice the story on your own a few times, but don't worry about memorizing it. Children like the story to develop slowly, and love to lend a hand in placing the patterns. Store all felt pieces flat in a large shoebox or shirt box. Organize and lay out your pieces in the order that they will appear on the board before you begin. Sit to the side of the board, and start slowly. And don't be afraid to add dramatic dimension when the spirit moves you!

Jack-o'-Lantern
An Original Halloween Tale

There once was a boy named Jack,
Pumpkin pie was his favorite snack.
(Place Jack on board, place pumpkin #1 next to Jack.)
One day he picked a pumpkin and said, "Granny, I've got a
    job for you.
(Place Granny on board, with table beside her.)
"Make me a pumpkin pie, and make it quick when you do!"
Well, pumpkin pie is a delicious food,
But the way Jack asked for it was really rude!
(Place pumpkin #1 on table.)
So Granny said, "Yes, pumpkin pie I can make with ease,
"But not until I hear you say 'please.' "
Well, that little boy Jack was an impatient sort.
He went outside to tease his black cat and scare little
    children just for sport.
(Move Jack aside, put black cat next to him, then place ghost
    over Jack.)
He put on Granny's white apron and then he yelled, "Boo!"
But wait for that pie he could no longer do!
He stomped up the stairs and in through the door.
(Remove ghost, place Jack next to Granny again.)
And said, "Give me my pie, Granny, I can't wait any more!"
Jack searched for his pie all over the place.
(Replace pumpkin #1 with pumpkin #2.)
Then he saw his pumpkin with a big painted face.
Granny had done it to let him know he was rude,
She thought next time he'd say "please" for his food.
But she was wrong! Jack said, "Granny! Just get along!"
What a boy that Jack could be! He said, "You must make that
    pie for me!"
(Move Jack aside again.)
Then he went outside—this time he took a broom for a ride.
(Replace Jack with witch, or place witch over him.)
He put on a black cape like a witch, and screamed!

He just liked to be mean and scare people, it seemed.
Then he stomped up the stairs again and in through the door.
(Remove witch, move Jack next to Granny again.)
And said, "Give me my pie, Granny, I can't wait any more!"
Jack was getting ruder and ruder by the minute:
"Make that pie, Granny, and put lots of sugar in it!"
But Granny just said, "Yes, pumpkin pie I can make with
    ease,
"But not until I hear you say 'please.' "
(Move Jack aside again.)
Granny sent Jack outside to play,
But soon he came in with something else to say.
He said, "This is taking so long, holy cow!
"Where is my pie? I want it now!"
(Remove pumpkin #2, put up curtain, return Jack.)
But there was no pie, that much was certain.
There was just an eerie glow behind an old curtain.
It was the pumpkin, carved, with a candle inside.
It glowed so prettily, Granny set it in the window with pride.
(Remove curtain, put up pumpkin #3.)
Looking at the pumpkin and at Granny, Jack understood.
He finally realized he'd been terribly rude.
"I'm sorry," he said to Granny, and gave her a squeeze.
"Now I know the only way to ask for something is to say
    'please!'
"Would you make me a pumpkin pie, pretty please?"
With a smile Granny handed Jack the pumpkin and said,
"This is a lantern, Jack.
(Place Granny and Jack close together.)
"Though it's dark you can go to the garden and bring another
    pumpkin back."
(Move Granny to side again, place pumpkin #3 near Jack's
    hands.)
Well, he did, and together they made a pumpkin pie that very
    night.
(Place pie on table.)
When Jack said, "Thank you," Granny smiled with delight.
And that is how jack-o'-lanterns came to be.
At least that's how Granny told it to me!

Pumpkin Face Shapes Activity

Materials: Black and orange construction paper, scraps of green construction paper, scissors, glue

Preparation: For each child cut six black triangles and six black squares. Distribute the shapes and give each child one sheet of orange paper and a small piece of green paper.

Activity: Have each child cut out a large circle from the orange paper. Have them create a pumpkin face on one side of the circle by gluing on only triangles for eyes, nose, and teeth. On the other side they can make another pumpkin face using only squares. Make an example of each face for the children to see. While they are working, help the children to identify the circle, squares, and triangles. Let them add a scrap of green paper to each pumpkin for a stem.

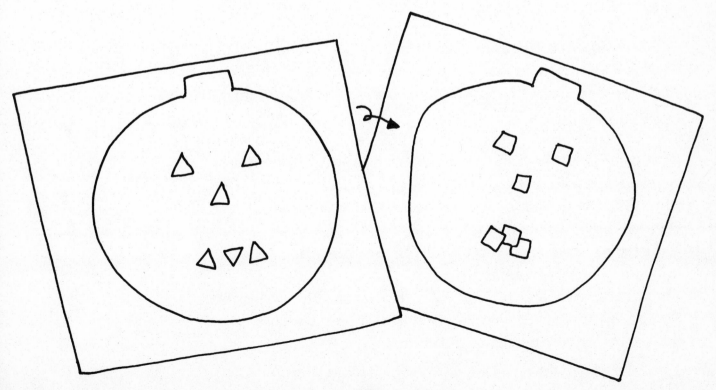

The Coming of the Corn
A Story Adapted from a Cheyenne Indian Folk Tale

An Indian boy and his mother lived alone in their tipi.
The boy was always hungry and very sleepy.
(Place tipi at center of board, trees at side.)
Each day the mother looked for food for dinner.
But she found nothing, and the boy kept growing thinner.
(Place mother and thin boy at sides of tipi.)
Then the mother went out gathering roots one day,
And another boy came by the tipi to play.
He was strong and healthy with cheeks big and round.
He appeared at the door of the tipi without a sound.
(Move mother off near trees, put up strong boy.)
The boy reached into his sack and took out a drum.
He said, "Come on, skinny one, let us dance and hum."
(Place drum on board.)
"I am skinny," said the boy, "because I have nothing to eat.
"I am too tired to dance on these skinny feet."
The chubby-cheeked boy danced and sang.
(Sing the following to "Twinkle, Twinkle, Little Star" and let
    the children join in.)
"Little boy is all alone, doesn't have a crumb or bone.
"If I tell him my secret, he might soon be eating it!
"Little boy is all alone, doesn't have a crumb or bone."
The boy finished his dance and song,
Then suddenly he and his drum were gone!
The mother returned and heard about the strong, healthy
    boy.
The fact that he might help them find food filled her with joy!
(Remove strong boy and drum, return mother to center.)
Before the mother left the next day,
She talked with her young son, and had this to say:
"Let the boy dance for you,
"But try to learn his secret when he is through."
(Move mother to trees again.)
The strong and healthy boy with cheeks so big and round,
Soon appeared at the tipi again without a sound.
(Place strong boy and rattle on board.)

This time he reached in his sack and took out a rattle.
He said, "Come on, skinny one, let's be wild, I won't tattle."
The chubby-cheeked boy danced and sang.
(Sing the following to the tune of "Twinkle, Twinkle, Little
    Star" and let the children join in.)
"Little boy is all alone, doesn't have a crumb or bone.
"If I tell him my secret, he might soon be eating it!
"Little boy is all alone, doesn't have a crumb or bone."
The boy finished his dance and song.
Then, suddenly, he and his rattle were gone!
(Remove strong boy and rattle, return mother.)
Again the boy told his mother, and this time she gave him a
    pocket of leather.
Inside he found a long, shiny feather.
(Place feather at boy's hand.)
The mother told her son, "Use this to tickle the boy until he
    tells you his tale.
"If he knows where to find food, we might follow his trail."
(Move mother near trees again.)
The strong and healthy boy with cheeks so big and round,
Soon appeared at the tipi again without a sound.
(Return strong boy, put on flute.)
This time he reached in his sack and took out a flute.
He said, "Come on, skinny one, let's holler and hoot!"
The chubby-cheeked boy started to sing.
(Sing the following to "Twinkle, Twinkle, Little Star.")
"Little boy is all alone, doesn't have a crumb or bone."
But something happened in the middle of his song.
The skinny boy took out his feather, so shiny and long.
And tickled the other boy in the tummy and rear.
Then finally he tickled the boy's puffy cheeks when he came
    near.
The chubby-cheeked boy had giggled slightly at first.
But when his puffy cheeks were tickled he laughed with a
    burst!
Something spilled out of those cheeks so round.
It spilled out and about all over the ground!
But the laugh was so shrill that the hungry boy closed his
    eyes,

And when he opened them again he was filled with surprise.
(Instruct the children to close their eyes; then remove the
    strong boy and flute, put on the corn, and say "Open your
    eyes!")
There was no more dancing, there was no more song.
Suddenly the big boy and his flute were gone.
But all over the ground was the strangest sight.
Grains of corn were scattered, so the thin boy tasted a bite.
He called for his mother to come and taste the grain.
(Return mother near boy.)
It was sweet and good, that much was plain.
They had never seen the strange grain before.
But after tasting it they knew they would be hungry no more.
The puffy-cheeked boy disappeared—it was quite strange.
They never saw him again, but things sure did change.
The mother and the boy had good grain to eat,
And every night from then on they had a great corn feast.
Then one day while at play the boy found things hidden in a
    tree.
There were the drum, the rattle, and the flute—all three!
(Place instruments on board.)
He took them home and sang his mother a song:
(Sing the following with the children to the tune of "Twinkle,
    Twinkle, Little Star.")
"Little boy left grains of corn, danced for me and sang a song.
"Then I ate the tasty corn, now I've grown so big and strong!"

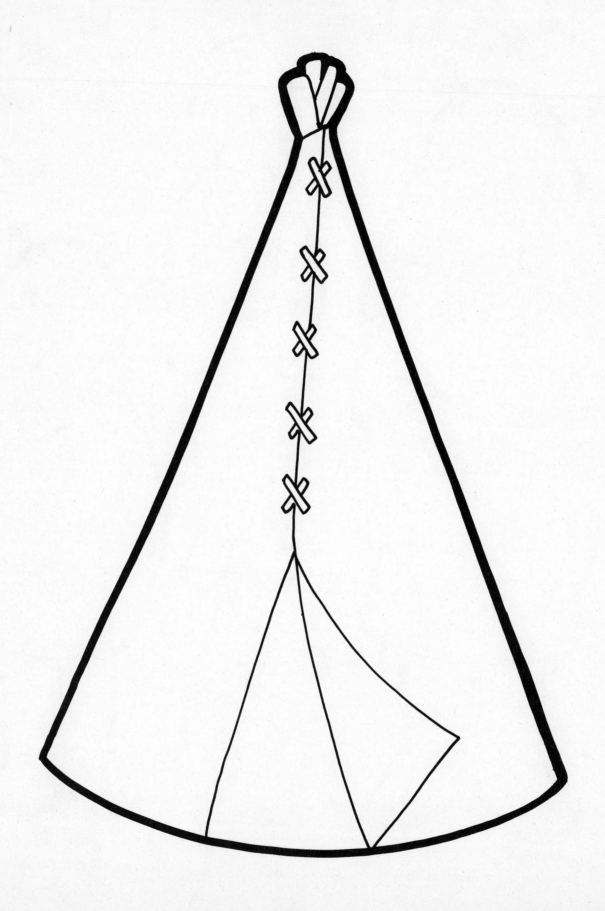

Movement Activity

Materials: Drum, rattle, flute

Preparation: Take the children to a large, open play area. You'll be using the instruments mentioned in the story to inspire some fun, improvisational dance and movement.

Activity: Have the children listen to the sounds you create with the instruments. First try a heavy, pounding drum beat. Encourage the children to "feel" the music and move their bodies in accordance with the sounds they hear. Let them stomp and jump if that is what they feel. The children might want to shake their bodies while you shake the rattle or twirl and make soft leaps while you play the flute. Allow plenty of time for the children to act out the different sounds and beats. Then give several children a chance to make the music while you join in the movement.

The Morning Before Christmas
An Original Christmas Tale

'Twas the morning before Christmas, and all through the
    house.
(Put on Christmas tree and mouse hole.)
Every creature was stirring, even Henry, the mouse.
(Put on Henry.)
Three thimbles were placed by the chimney with care,
In hopes that St. Nicholas soon would be there.
(Put on mantle, point to three thimbles and count them.)
Papa had just hopped up from his bed,
Thinking of thimbles of cheese and crusts of old bread.
(Put on Papa.)
And Mama in her booties and Henry in his cap
Had just gone to the kitchen to check for the cat.
(Put on Mama near Henry.)
When out in the treetop they heard such a chatter,
(Put tree on other side of board.)
The cat was chasing the birds and making them scatter!
(Put on cat, put two birds in sky.)
Away to the mouse hole Henry flew like a flash,
Threw some water at the cat, and away the cat dashed!
(Move Henry near hole, make a splashing noise, remove cat.)
The birds in the tree were thankful, I know.
(Move birds back to treetop.)
For they dropped three nuts down to Henry, below.
(Put three nuts on ground, count them, then move them
    inside.)
Well, now that the danger was past and all was clear,
Henry and his parents went to work baking Christmas cheer.
They made cookies, and cakes, and pretty lollipops.
And put all the goodies in a specially wrapped box.
(Put on ribboned box.)
Then there was a jingling and a flurry of snow.
(Shake some jingle bells, throw out a handful of confetti.)
What could it be? The mice didn't know.

Then someone said, "To the side of the wall!
"To get in this mouse hole, I must be very small!"
(Put large Santa outside near tree.)
The mice had baked so long, through the day and night,
They didn't realize the time—it was Christmas Eve, all right!
They heard Santa's voice, and ran off to bed,
Leaving the boxful of goodies for St. Nick as they fled.
(Lay the three mice side by side.)
And then, just like magic, they fell fast asleep,
Papa, Mama, and Henry, all in a heap.
As Henry was snoring and rolling around.
(Make a snoring sound.)
Through the hole Santa squeezed, without a sound.
(Remove large Santa, replace with tiny Santa inside hole.)
He went to the thimbles and filled them with cheese.
He dropped bread crumbs and crackers under the tree.
He left mouse toys and mittens and treats for all three,
(Put teddy bear near tree.)
And he smiled when he saw them, all sleeping with ease.
Then his eyes, how they widened! His dimples twitched!
For the cat waited outside—this was a hitch!
(Put on cat.)
Santa's little pink mouth went into a frown.
How would he get to the other children in town?
The cat was coming nearer, its nose to the ground.
(Move cat nearer to hole.)
Nearer and nearer—but what was that sound?
The birds were diving and pecking the cat!
They pecked it and drove it away just like that!
(Put birds down near cat.)
The cat gave a howl and hissed as it fled.
(Remove cat, move birds back to treetop.)
Then Santa knew he had nothing to dread.
He sighed with relief, in spite of himself.
Santa was happy, a thankful old elf.
He sampled the goodies and finished his work,

He looked out the hole, then squeezed through with a jerk.
(Remove tiny Santa, put large Santa and ribboned box
    outside.)
And standing close to the trunk of the tree
He left some bread and special birdseed.
(Put Santa and bag of seed near tree trunk.)
Then, in a twinkling, he was gone from sight,
Flying away with a sparkle of light.
(Throw handful of glitter into the air, remove Santa and
    ribboned box.)
He shouted one thing, then was gone just like that:
"Happy Christmas to all, and watch out for the cat!"

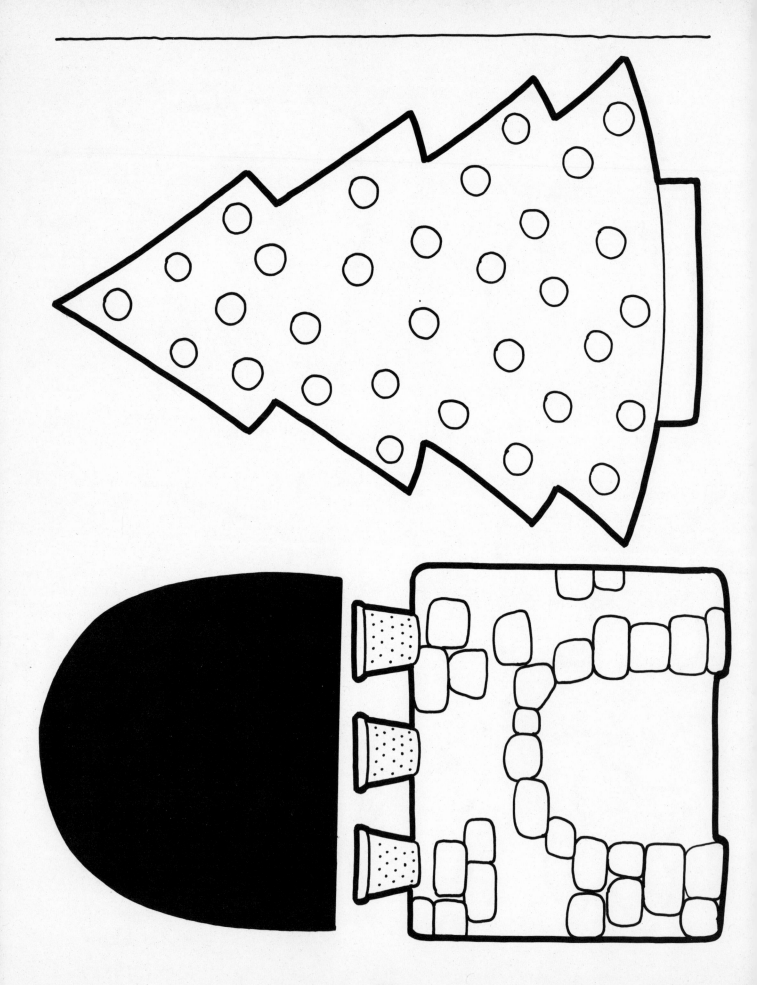

SEED

28

Cat and Mouse Game

Materials: Gray felt, small gray pompons, short lengths of tan or gray yarn, black markers or small black sequins, black paper, scissors, glue, coffee can, flat crackers, die

Preparation: Cut out and glue together a simple cat shape from the black paper. Cover the coffee can— the mouse hole—with another piece of black paper.

Activity: First have each child make a small mouse to use in the game. Show them how to cut the felt into a small teardrop shape. Then let them glue on a pompon and a length of yarn for a tail. They may glue on sequins for eyes, or draw eyes on with markers. Next, turn the coffee can on its side and place it on a table. Place about a dozen crackers leading up to the mouse hole. Then let each child roll the die and move his or her mouse that number of crackers. After each child has had a turn, roll the die and move the cat the correct number of crackers. Let play continue, encouraging the children to try to move their mice into the mouse hole before the cat gets there. The game ends when the cat reaches the mouse hole or when all the mice have safely entered. Let everyone nibble on crackers for a post-game snack.

The Magic Mortar
Adapted from a Japanese New Year's Folk Tale

Note: Before you begin this flannel board story, show the children a rice cake and demonstrate how a mortar and pestle work.

(Put on hut, poor man, house, rich man.)
A poor man had no food as the New Year drew near.
It would be a sad holiday, that much was clear.
The man's rich brother wouldn't share.
He was selfish with his rice, and just didn't care.
(Hold up a grain of rice, shrug, and throw it over your
    shoulder.)
Then the poor brother met a man, very old and kind.
"Listen to me," he said, "and see what good luck you'll find."
(Put on old man and rice cake near bottom, move poor man
    close to them.)
"Go deep into the forest and find the little gnomes.
"Then trade this rice cake for their mortar made of stone.
"You'll see that it will work magic for you.
"Just use it wisely, whatever you do."
(Place rice cake next to poor man, put gnomes off to side.)
The man thought of feeding the rice cake to his family
    instead,
But he felt he must do as the old man had said.
He searched and searched and searched for the gnomes.
He found them in their tiny forest homes.
They smiled when they smelled the good cake made of rice.
(Remove the old man, move poor man and rice cake next to
    gnomes.)
"Give it to us," they demanded, "an early dinner would be
    nice!"
"It is not mine to give you," said the poor man.
"I was told to trade it for your mortar, if I can!"
(Put on mortar.)
"How did you know of the mortar?" they all cried.
"It's our secret—and how did you know where we hide?"

The creatures thought the man must be powerful, indeed,
So they handed over their mortar with surprising speed.
(Put mortar next to man, rice cake next to gnomes.)
The poor man quickly fled home with his prize.
And there all you could hear were joyful cries!
It would now be a happy Japanese New Year—that was clear!
(Put man and mortar next to hut, put on rice bowls.)
For the man whispered, "Oh, magic mortar, hear my plea.
"Make rice for my hungry family and me."
And instantly the rice bowls were as full as could be!
The family was grateful, and the man didn't wish for a lot.
Just every so often he'd ask for more rice or a new pot.
(Put on pot.)
But the greedy brother heard of his poor brother's trick,
And he stole the mortar, lickity split!
(Move mortar near greedy brother's house.)
He wished for sparkling piles of gold,
(Put on gold.)
He wished and he wished for treasure to hold.
Then he snuck away and took the mortar to sea in a boat.
But he forgot, in his greed, that gold doesn't float!
(Put rich man in boat, add gold.)
He wished and he wished, till his boat started to sink.
But he was so full of greed that he just couldn't think!
He wanted more gold, he just couldn't wait.
But he didn't stop wishing until it was too late.
(Shake head, remove boat and gold, put man on log.)
As his boat went under he started to frown.
He grabbed onto some driftwood as he started to drown.
Crying for his gold, he drifted far out to sea.
It is not good to be greedy, that you can see!
(Put mortar near shore, move greedy man near good brother
    as you read.)
The mortar soon washed up on the shore.
The good brother found it, and it was his ever more.
The New Year was happy, the greedy brother was saved.
And it was amazing how much better he behaved!

Rice Cake Printing

Materials: Dry rice cakes, fluorescent colored paints, black construction paper, medium-sized googly eyes, yarn, pie pans, glue, newspaper

Preparation: Pour a different color of paint into each pie tin. Give each child a sheet of black paper.

Activity: Have the children press the bottom surface of their rice cake into paint and then press on paper, working on newspaper first for practice. When they are ready, let the children make a few prints on the black paper and let them dry. They may create funny creatures by gluing googly eyes to the rice cake prints and gluing on bits of yarn for arms and legs.

The Big-Hearted Elephant
An Original Valentine's Day Story

There is a deep dark jungle far, far away.
Here the animals romp, run, and play.
There are vines and shrubs and trees of green,
(Put on berry bush on one side.)
But the king of the jungle is ferocious and mean!
(Put the lion off to the other side.)
He's a great big lion with a crown and a throne,
(Put on throne, put crown on lion's head.)
He roars, "In *my* jungle *I'm* the king of my home!"
But there are other animals who live with the king.
There's a hippo, and a snake who's a slithery thing.
There's a funny little monkey who likes to swing.
There's a tall giraffe, and a huge elephant who's a lumbering
    thing.
(Place each animal on as it is named, ending with the
    elephant at the far edge of the board, away from the lion.)
They're ordinary animals in the ordinary way,
But the elephant is different, and he's teased every day.
You see, he has great floppy ears that are pink on the
    underside,
(Put on heart-shaped ears, gray side showing and pointing up.)
And the animals can never keep from laughing, no matter
    how hard they try.
His ears are so silly, a ridiculous sight,
And the elephant is sad that his ears just aren't right.
Well, one special day the animals were at the pond's shore.
They startled when they heard the old lion's roar.
It was Valentine's Day, and they wanted to give him a gift.
Lately he was so nasty they thought a gift might give him a lift.
But a jungle is not like our own town.
There are no candies, no presents, no balloons to be found!
But the smart little monkey had a bright plan:
(Move monkey to the berry bush.)
"Why, we'll mash up some berries as quick as we can.
"Then we'll paint on some hearts for a Valentine's card.
"We can paint on each other, that wouldn't be hard!"
And before you know it, the animals did just that.

37

They painted on hearts, they painted this way and that!
(Let children place some small hearts on the animals.)
They hoped the lion would like it—they were a little afraid.
But they got themselves ready for a Valentine's parade.
They lined up real straight: the hippo, the monkey, the
    giraffe, the elephant, and, finally, the snake.
(Point at each animal as you speak.)
But all of a sudden it started to rain!
(Put up rain cloud.)
The hearts all washed off, it was a terrible shame.
(Remove the small hearts.)
But off on the side stood someone quiet and shy.
It was the elephant, and he gave a big sigh.
"Oh, what isssss it?" said the snake, coming near.
(Place snake by the elephant's feet.)
She joked, Got sssssomething sssstuck in your ear?"
Then everyone laughed and giggled and grinned,
But the elephant just smiled, this time it didn't bother him.
"I have an idea," he said, full of pride. "You know, my ears
    are pink on the underside."
(Turn up just a pink corner of an ear.)
The snake spoke right up: "And pink'ssssss for
    Valentine'ssssssss Day!"
Then everyone clapped and shouted, "Hooray!"
They knew what to do, they didn't waste any time.
The monkey went hunting for a good sturdy vine.
Since giraffe was the tallest she tied the ears up tight.
(Turn the ears over to show the pink sides.)
Then everyone stared at the marvelous sight.
They'd never seen such beautiful Valentine ears,
And the elephant smiled when he heard the loud cheers.
Then they all saw the old lion stomping their way.
(Place lion near other animals.)
They got very excited—what would he say?
Well, the lion was so happy he gave the elephant his crown!
(Place crown above elephant's ears.)
Everyone clapped, and then humbly bowed down.
So if you ever see a person with big ears or a big nose,
With silly looking hair or funny looking clothes,
Don't ever tease, and don't ever stare,
Because the outside isn't always the only thing there!

Cut 4 heart-shaped ear patterns: make 2 gray, 2 pink. Glue one of each color together for each ear.

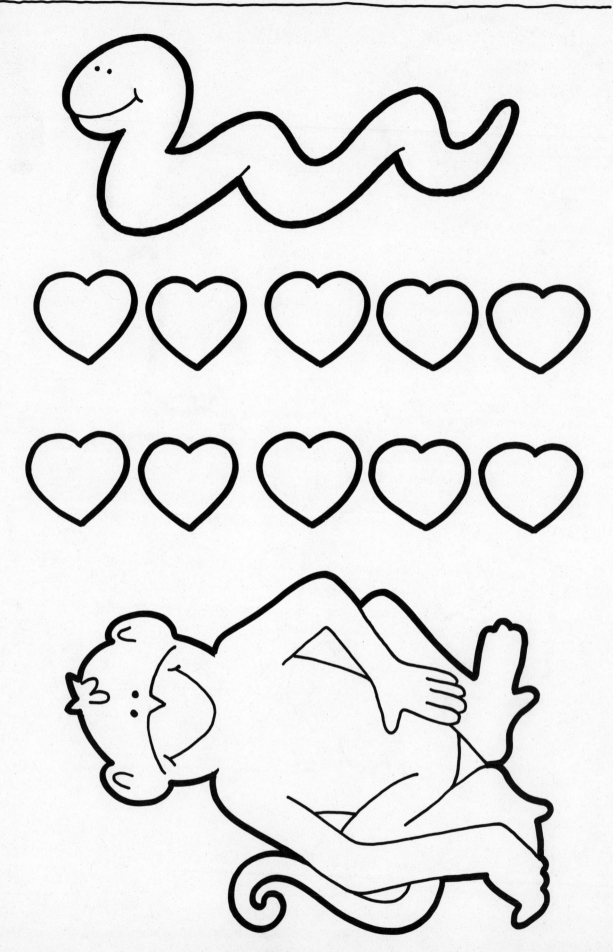

Color Combining Experiment

Materials: White, black, and red paint; large sheet of white paper; small bowls; paintbrushes; marker; three small measuring cups with spout

Preparation: Use the marker to outline a large elephant head on the white paper. Place a small amount of one color of paint in each measuring cup.

Activity: The children will work together to color in the big-hearted elephant you outlined, painting the ears pink and the trunk and face gray. Begin by asking them to name the colors in the cups; they will see there is no pink or gray. Encourage the children to think about how they might come up with the right colors from the ones available. If a child offers, let him or her demonstrate how to mix the colors to make pink or gray. Or you might pose the question, "I wonder what would happen if I mixed black and white?"—and then do it. Let each child have a hand at mixing colors in a bowl to come up with the desired shades he or she wishes to use. Then have the children paint away!

The April Fool's Race with Toad and Donkey
Adapted from an Afro-American Folk Tale

One day the Master King of the land decided to have a big April Fool's race.

He promised to give a special prize to whoever came in first place.

(Put on trophy and finish flagstand at far right.)

Both Toad and Donkey decided to enter the game.

Toad knew Donkey was fast, but he liked racing just the same.

Donkey said, "Toad, you're small and powerless,

"How you think you can win this race, I just couldn't guess!"

(Put on Donkey and Toad at far left.)

Well, the race course was set out along the road,

Twenty miles long—it looked awfully far for little Toad.

Donkey kept boasting and bragging about his speed.

Toad got tired of this and thought, "A plan is what I need!"

So before the race Toad talked to his children—twenty little toads!

They looked just like him, so he hid them all along the road!

(Put up start flag.)

When the flag went up Donkey kicked up dirt and sped away.

Then he thought, "I'm so fast I can eat some grass along the way!"

(Move Donkey a little way off, put grass beneath his nose.)

He was so sure of himself he took an hour to go the first mile.

Of course, Toad had hidden away in the bushes all this while!

(Remove Toad, put on milepost #1.)

Donkey bawled out at the first milepost, "Ha! Ha! Ha! I'm better than Toad!"

Then he heard a very familiar sound right near him on the road.

Toad's first child called out, like all toads do, "Rib-bok! Rib-bok!"

(Put Donkey at milepost #1, put baby toad next to it.)

Donkey was flabbergasted and wondered, "How can I be
    hearing Toad talk?"
Now Donkey was angry, switching his tail like a horsewhip.
He raced off thinking, "I can't eat any more grass on this
    trip!"
(Move Donkey a little way off, place carrots beneath his nose.)
Still, as he raced along he thought, "I can't lose with just a
    few stops."
So he paused by the side of the road to munch a few carrot tops.
(Put on milepost #2.)
When he stopped eating, Donkey bawled out at the second
    milepost, "Ha! Ha! Ha! I'm better than Toad!"
And again he heard a very familiar sound on the road.
Toad's second child called out, like all toads do, "Rib-bok!
    Rib-bok!"
(Move Donkey to milepost #2, place a baby toad next to it.)
Donkey was even more flabbergasted—"How can I be hearing
    Toad talk?
"I'll have to kick up that hard, hard dirt faster than I thought.
"Otherwise I fear that I will certainly be caught!"
This time Donkey sped off like lightning on his way,
And he didn't stop to snack on a thing along the way.
(Put on milepost #3.)
Then once again Donkey bawled out, almost breathless, at
    the third milepost, "Ha! Ha! Ha! I'm better than Toad!"
And again he heard a very familiar sound on the road.
Toad's third child called out, like all toads do, "Rib-bok!
    Rib-bok!"
(Move Donkey to milepost #3, place a baby toad next to it.)
And Donkey was even more flabbergasted—"How can I be
    hearing Toad talk?"
Well, this went on and on, and finally old Donkey got plain
    sad in his mind.
He trotted on for a while, but then got angry and simply gave
    up after a time.
(Shake head, remove Donkey, place Toad at finish with
    trophy.)
Well, Toad tricked Donkey—Toad liked playing April Fool's
    jokes.
But even after he got his prize, he never did boast!

Five Little Warty Toads Action Verse

Preparation: After hearing the flannel board story, let five children at a time act out this fun counting verse. Line the children up, letting each be a toad in the verse. Let them "rib-bok" in turn, then, one by one, curl their hands under their heads to sleep. Or have the group recite the verse together, holding out the appropriate number of fingers for toads and "rib-bok"-ing in unison. You may want to present the verse as a mini-play.

Verse:

Five little warty toads, can't you hear them talk?
Rib-bok! Rib-bok! Rib-bok! Rib-bok! Rib-bok!
One went to sleep and then there were four!
Four little warty toads, can't you hear them talk?
Rib-bok! Rib-bok! Rib-bok! Rib-bok!
One went to sleep and then there were three!
Three little warty toads, can't you hear them talk?
Rib-bok! Rib-bok! Rib-bok!
One went to sleep and then there were two!
Two little warty toads, can't you hear them talk?
Rib-bok! Rib-bok!
One went to sleep and then there was one!
One little warty Toad, can't you hear him talk?
Rib-bok!
One went to sleep and now there is none!

The First Easter Bunny
Adapted from a German Legend

It was almost Easter Sunday in a tiny German town,
But the mothers there were sad, their faces full of frowns.
They were poor and had no sweets
Though they knew their children loved Easter treats.
(Put on patches of bushy grass and two mothers.)
The morning was bright with a big, glowing sun,
So the mothers set out their baskets, because the chores had
    to be done.
(Put on sun and two baskets.)
They gathered the chicken eggs hidden in grass so tall.
They hunted and hunted until they found them all.
(Let the children place the little eggs, one by one, in the
    baskets.)
Soon their baskets were full with round, white eggs.
So they stopped for a while to rest their tired legs.
"Egg, eggs, nothing but eggs!" said one mother.
(Point to all the eggs.)
"There must be something else for our children," said
    another.
"Easter is a time for treats," they said with a sigh.
"We must think of a surprise, we really must try!"
Then someone had an idea that was truly quite bright.
It looked like Easter Sunday would turn out all right!
They would make a special game for the children on Easter
    day.
They would set up an egg hunt and let the children play.
(Remove baskets and eggs, pretend to hide eggs behind the
    grass.)
They hid their white eggs again in the grass and the trees.
They hid them so well that they couldn't be seen.
Still, the mothers wished they could hide something special or
    new,
But they knew the white eggs were the best they could do.
(Put on bunny off to side.)
All this time there was someone hiding in the grass nearby.

It was a great big bunny and he hated to hear the mothers
    sigh.
This bunny was special because he was very smart.
He was friendly, too, with a kind heart.
(Remove mothers.)
Soon the mothers left to check on their children at play,
And the bunny started right in with his plan for the next day.
He gathered up berries and flowers with colors so bright.
Then he mashed them all up to make paint that was just
    right.
(Put up bowls of paint.)
For brushes he collected cattails, just the right size.
Then he started to work on the Easter surprise.
The children went to sleep that night, and closed their little
    eyes.
Now you must do the same and wait for the surprise!
(Instruct the children to close their eyes for a moment, then
    remove the bunny and paints and lay out all the giant eggs
    so the children can help put them on the board.)
When the children woke up in the morning they were sent out
    to hunt.
But they sure didn't know about the bunny's clever stunt.
(Put on two children, then let children in class put on each
    egg as it is named.)
The eggs in the grass were no longer white!
They were giant sized, and beautifully bright!
There were striped ones, dotted ones, and flowered ones too.
But where they had come from, nobody knew!
There were red ones and green ones and yellow ones too.
There were even chocolate ones—yes, chocolate, it's true!
(Put bunny up again.)
In the middle of the excitement something rustled nearby.
And there went the big bunny, hopping on by.
The children all yelled, "It must be a trick!
"These eggs wouldn't come from any old chick!
"They're bunny eggs!" the children cried.
"Until next Easter!" the bunny yelled back, and ran off to
    hide!

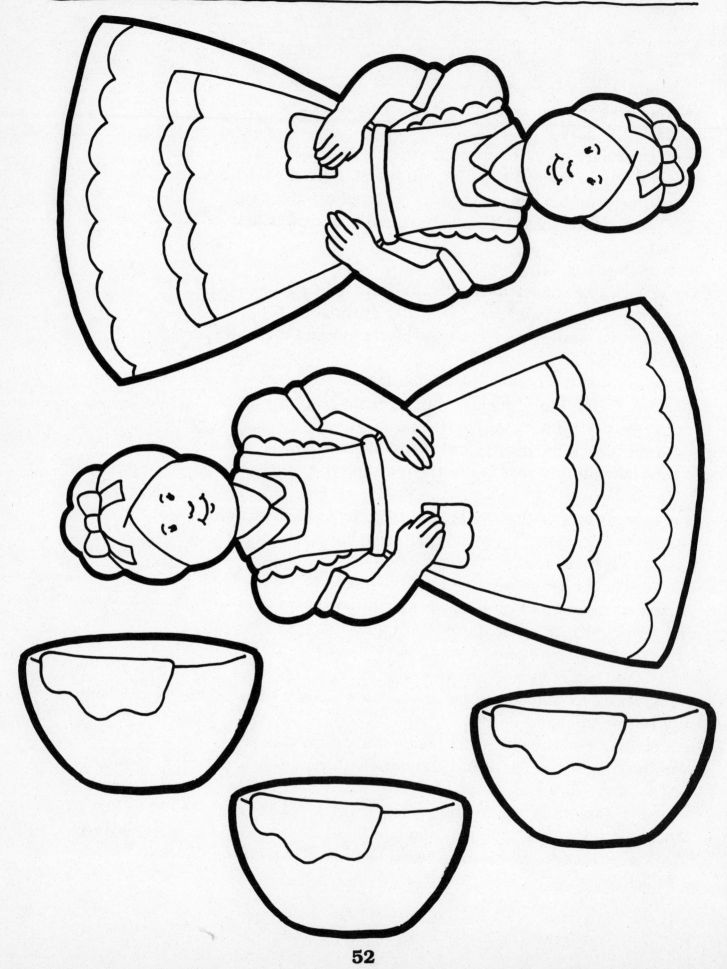

Egg Match-Up Activity

Materials: Large pieces of black construction paper; white construction paper; red, green, yellow, blue, and orange crayons; glue; scissors

Preparation: Cut out ten egg shapes for each child from the white paper. Color one egg from each set red, one green, one yellow, one with blue stripes, and one with orange dots.

Activity: Have each child glue each of the colored eggs onto black paper. Then let the children use the crayons to make a matching egg for each one just glued down. Have the children glue the second red egg beside the first red egg, the second blue-striped egg beside the first blue-striped one, and so on.

How the Sun Came to Be
Adapted from a North American Indian Tale

Once, a mighty magician put the stars, moon, and sun each
   in a box.
(Place magician in upper right corner.)
He put on the lids, and snapped on the locks.
(Place three boxes near magician.)
The boxes were marked 1, 2, and 3.
The magician put them in a cave where no one could see.
(Point to boxes while counting.)
The magician kept the light out of sight.
It was quiet everywhere, and dark as night.
There was only the dark sea.
There was only the dark forest of trees.
The magician had love in his heart for almost no one.
But there was one baby boy he loved like a son.
(Place baby on board.)
The baby boy was clever, he was also very strong.
To the magician's mind he did nothing wrong.
But unlike the magician, the boy wanted to do what was
   right.
As he got older, he decided he must bring his people the light.
(Replace baby with boy.)
The boy went to the magician, he knew just what to do.
He asked for the boxes marked number 1 and number 2.
(Point to boxes while counting.)
At first the magician said no.
But the boy cried and begged—it was terrific as tantrums go!
Finally the magician said, "These are *my* boxes, marked 1, 2,
   and 3.
"As you know, they are very dear to me!
"You may play with the boxes marked number 1 and 2.
"But do not open them, whatever you do!"
(Point to the boxes while counting, then move boxes 1 and 2
   down near boy.)

The boy played with the boxes carefully at first.

But when the magician wasn't looking, he opened them with a burst!

Out came millions of stars, sparkling white.

Out came a big yellow moon, glowing with light.

(Place stars and moon up in the sky.)

They flew up and up, really quite high,

And the people were amazed with the wonder in the sky.

The magician stomped and screamed, "What, what did you do?

"The light can never be put back into boxes 1 and 2!"

(Try to stuff stars and moon in boxes, then shrug and return them to sky.)

Now, the magician was angry for days and for weeks.

But finally he forgave the boy, and pinched his pink cheeks.

(Pinch a child's cheeks nearby.)

Soon the boy asked to play with the box marked number 3.

It held the sun, the greatest light of the three.

The magician said, "I can't give you that box, it would be foolish, that's true."

But the boy threw a tantrum until he was blue!

Finally, the magician gave him the box, saying, "This is *my* box, marked number 3.

"As you know, it is very dear to me!

"You may play with the box marked number 3.

"But do not open it—do you see?"

(Point to the box each time it's mentioned, then move it near the boy.)

The boy played with it carefully at first.

Then, when the magician wasn't looking, he opened it with a burst!

Out came the brightest, most beautiful gold light!

It was so wondrous, it gave everyone a fright!

(Place the sun in the sky.)

It flew up and up, really quite high.

And the people were amazed at the wonder in the sky.

The magician stomped and screamed, "What, what do I see?

"The sun can never be put back into box number 3!"

(Try to fit sun back into box, then shrug and place it back in
   the sky.)

But the people were happy the boy had brought them these
   prizes.

Boxes 1, 2, and 3 had held such surprises!

(Line up the boxes in order.)

The magician remained the only sad one.

He grumbled every day about losing the sun.

He muttered, "Boxes! Boxes 1, 2, and 3!

"Boxes! Boxes! All gone from me!"

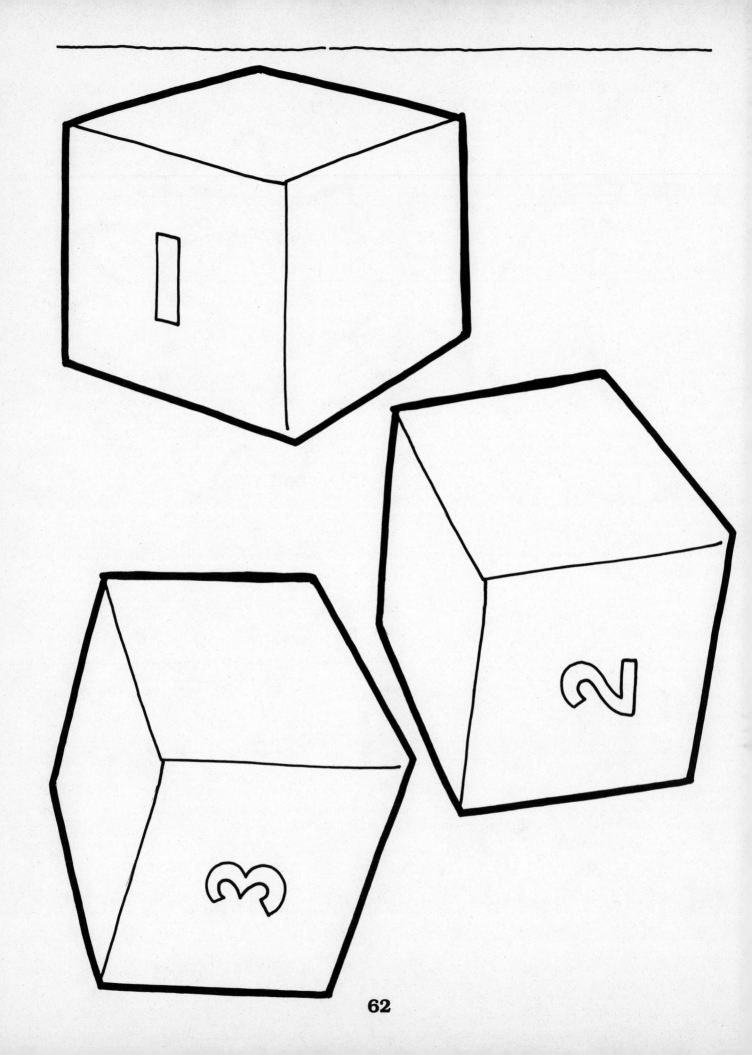

Star Counting Activity

Materials: Index cards, adhesive stars, muffin tins

Preparation: Place a number of stars in the sections of the muffin tins. Then make a set of ten star cards, each containing a number group from one to ten (you may want to make each number group a different color to give the children a color cue, for example, two green stars, three red stars, four silver stars, and so on). Give each child ten blank index cards and a star-filled muffin tin.

Activity: Place the card with one star on it before the children at a low table. Have them copy the number group by pressing on the correct number of stars. Continue with each number group through ten.

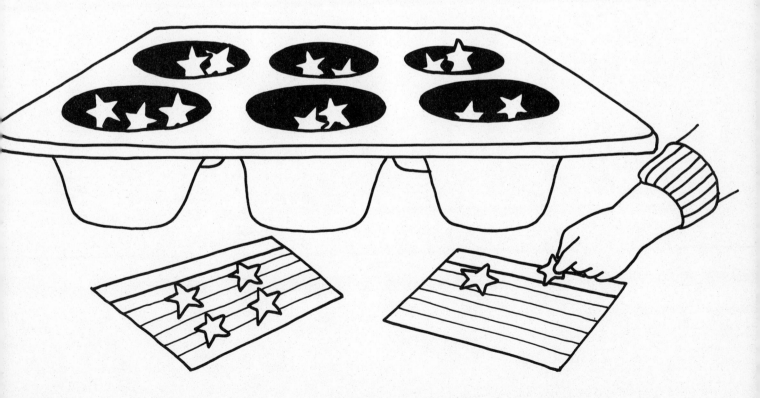

Resources

Aliki, *Corn Is Maize*, Harper & Row, 1976.

Baylor, Byrd, *I'm In Charge of Celebrations*, Scribner's, 1986.

Cole, Joanna, *Best-Loved Folktales of the World*, Doubleday, 1982.

Hamilton, Virginia, *The People Could Fly, American Black Folktales*, Knopf, 1985.

Kronberg, Ruthilde, and McKissack, Patricia C., *A Piece of the Wind*, Harper & Row, 1990.

Retan, Walter, *Favorite Tales from Many Lands*, Grosset and Dunlap, 1989.